Join in
Jump

Join in — Jump on!

Scripture Union
207-209 Queensway, Bletchley, Milton Keynes, MK2 2EB, UK
Email: info@scriptureunion.org.uk
Website: www.scriptureunion.org.uk

Scripture Union Australia
Locked Bag 2, Central Coast Business Centre, NSW 2252
Website: www.su.org.au

Scripture Union USA
P. O. Box 987, Valley Forge, PA 19482
www.scriptureunion.org

Writers: Margaret Cluley, Sue Dunn, Jean Elliott, Muriel Griffith, Susanne and Mark Hopkins, Christine Wright

Editor: Marjory Francis
Design: Chris Gander Design Associates Illustration: Branwen Thomas

ISBN 185999 387 7
© Scripture Union 2000, reprinted 2003

Printed and bound in the UK by Ebenezer Baylis & Son Ltd, The Trinity Press, Worcester and London

Scriptures quoted from the Contemporary English Version
© American Bible Society 1991,1992,1995. Anglicisation © British & Foreign Bible Society, 1996. Used with permission.

Join in — Jump on! will work best if used alongside the CEV or GNB.

Scripture Union is an international Christian charity working with churches in more than 130 countries, providing resources to bring the good news about Jesus Christ to children, young people and families and to encourage them to develop spiritually through the Bible and prayer.

As well as our network of volunteers, staff and associates who run holidays, church-based events and school Christian groups, we produce a wide range of publications and support those who use our resources through training programmes.

To help you

Did you know the Bible is made up of lots of books?
You will be reading from these books in **Join in – Jump on!**
Genesis   Exodus   1 Kings   Psalms
See if you can find them in the Old Testament books below and colour
them in.

Genesis | Exodus | Leviticus | Numbers | Deuteronomy | Joshua | Judges | Ruth | 1 Samuel | 2 Samuel | 1 Kings | 2 Kings | 1 Chronicles | 2 Chronicles | Ezra | Nehemiah | Esther | Job | Psalms | Proverbs | Ecclesiastes | Song of Songs | Isaiah | Jeremiah | Lamentations | Ezekiel | Daniel | Hosea | Joel | Amos | Obadiah | Jonah | Micah | Nahum | Habakkuk | Zephaniah | Haggai | Zechariah | Malachi

Now see if you can find and colour the ones you will be reading from the
New Testament.
John   Acts   2 Corinthians   Philippians   2 Thessalonians   Philemon

Matthew | Mark | Luke | John | Acts | Romans | 1 Corinthians | 2 Corinthians | Galatians | Ephesians | Philippians | Colossians | 1 Thessalonians | 2 Thessalonians | 1 Timothy | 2 Timothy | Titus | Philemon | Hebrews | James | 1 Peter | 2 Peter | 1 John | 2 John | 3 John | Jude | Revelation

In this book find out about:

People Jesus met *Days 1 to 4*
Joseph *Days 5 to 15*
I can pray for other people *Days 16 to 21*
Onesimus *Days 22 to 23*
The place to meet God *Days 24 to 31*
Jesus does amazing things *Days 32 to 40*
Pictures of Jesus *Days 41 to 45*
Abraham *Days 46 to 50*

Plus:
Lots of Extra pages
All over the world!
The joke and puzzle page!

How to use this book

There are Bible activities in this book to keep you busy for 50 days. You will find stories about people in the Bible and lots of ideas to help you get to know God better. Each day you will find:

- something to read
- a puzzle or questions to answer
- something to look up in the Bible
- a prayer idea

Sometimes there are Extra fun ideas too!

Here are some ideas for using **Join in – Jump on!**

- It's best to read it every day if you can, but it doesn't matter if you miss days sometimes. Just carry on from where you got up to.
- It's OK to use **Join in – Jump on!** on your own, or you might like someone to help you.
- Most days you will just need a Bible and a pencil to use with **Join in – Jump on!**
- It's best to save the Extra pages for when you have lots of time. You will need to collect other things to use for these.
- Try to find somewhere quiet to read your Bible and **Join in – Jump on!**

So make sure you have a Bible and a pencil, and jump on to **Join in – Jump on!** now!

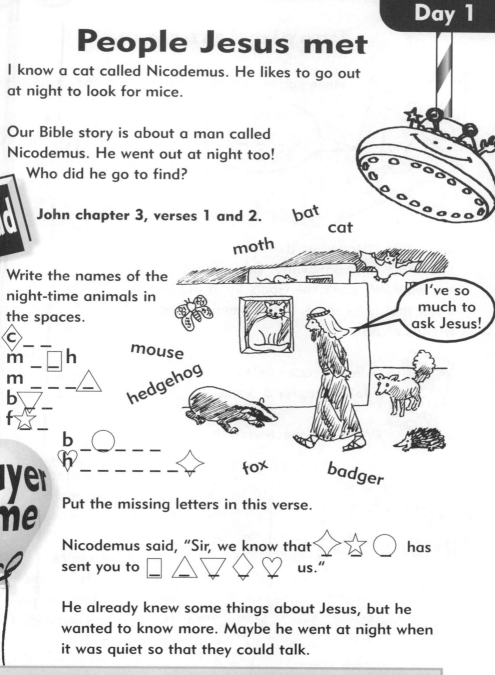

People Jesus met

I know a cat called Nicodemus. He likes to go out at night to look for mice.

Our Bible story is about a man called Nicodemus. He went out at night too!
Who did he go to find?

read

John chapter 3, verses 1 and 2.

bat

cat

moth

Write the names of the night-time animals in the spaces.

c _ _
m _ □ h
m _ _ _ _ △
b ▽ _ _
f ☆ _

mouse

hedgehog

b _ ○ _ _ _ _
h _ _ _ _ _ _ ✧

fox

badger

I've so much to ask Jesus!

Prayer time

Put the missing letters in this verse.

Nicodemus said, "Sir, we know that ◇ ☆ ○ has sent you to □ △ ▽ ◇ ♡ us."

He already knew some things about Jesus, but he wanted to know more. Maybe he went at night when it was quiet so that they could talk.

Dear Lord Jesus, I know some things about you, but I would like to get to know you better. Please help me to find times when I can be quiet with you.

☑

Day 2

People Jesus met

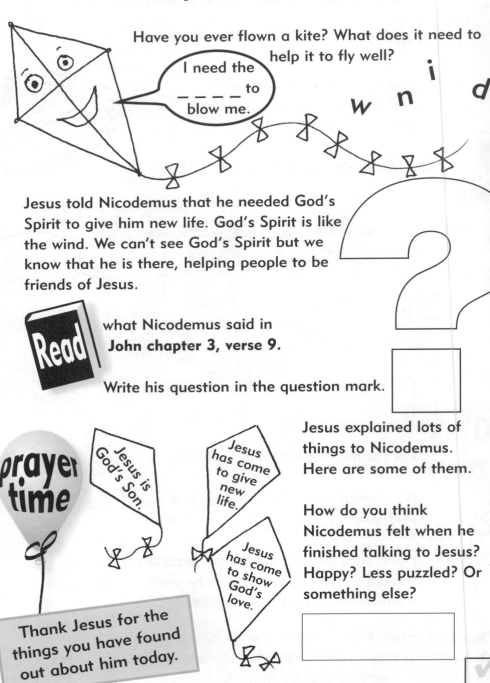

Have you ever flown a kite? What does it need to help it to fly well?

I need the _ _ _ _ to blow me.

w n i d

Jesus told Nicodemus that he needed God's Spirit to give him new life. God's Spirit is like the wind. We can't see God's Spirit but we know that he is there, helping people to be friends of Jesus.

Read what Nicodemus said in **John chapter 3, verse 9.**

Write his question in the question mark.

prayer time

Jesus is God's Son.

Jesus has come to give new life.

Jesus has come to show God's love.

Thank Jesus for the things you have found out about him today.

Jesus explained lots of things to Nicodemus. Here are some of them.

How do you think Nicodemus felt when he finished talking to Jesus? Happy? Less puzzled? Or something else?

People Jesus met

Imagine it is the middle of the day. The sun is very hot and you have been walking all morning. You sit down to rest. What would you like most of all?

Jesus was resting by a well when someone came.

John chapter 4, verses 6 to 8. Write what Jesus asked the woman.

Here's what happened next:

Sir, I'm surprised you're asking a foreigner like me for a drink!

a prayer

Jesus talked to the lady about God and about herself.

Sir! You know all about me! You must be a prophet. I know that one day God will send a very special person to us!

That's me! I'm talking to you now!

Dear Lord Jesus, you talked with Nicodemus at night-time and the Samaritan woman in the middle of the day. You had time for both of them. Thank you for always having time for me!

What would you have done? Find out on Day 4 what the Samaritan woman did.

People Jesus met

Read what the Samaritan woman did in **John chapter 4, verses 28 to 30.**

Look at her!

Come with me! Come and see! Come and meet a man who is special!

What is she on about?

I've never seen her so excited!

We'd better go and see for ourselves.

prayer time

Everyone in town went out to see Jesus

We and are is are certain we sure that and
the is is the of Saviour of and the the is wo

Colour in all the uncracked water pots to find out what the people said.

Have you ever told anyone about Jesus? Many people still don't know how special he is. Thank God that every day more people hear about Jesus, and ask God to help you tell your friends about him.

Star Mobile

Ask an adult to help you cut out fifteen card star-shapes. Decorate one side of each star with gold or silver paper, sequins or glitter.

Jesus said something very important when he was talking to Nicodemus. He said, "God loved the people of this world so much that he gave his only Son."

Write one word from the verse on the back of each star. Put some thread on the stars and hang them from a stick or coat-hanger like this:

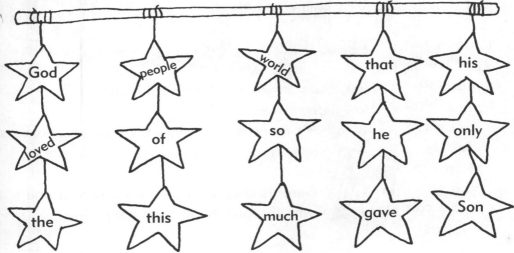

Joseph

"Hello, I'm Joseph. I am old now, but what I did when I was younger is a very exciting story. I'll write it down for you a little at a time. The trouble is, I sometimes fall asleep as I'm writing, so you may have to look in the Bible to find out the end of the story." (Look out for the zzzs!)

a prayer

Thank you, Lord God, that you have a plan for every family. Happy or sad, you always care for us.

"First, count how many brothers I had."

"How many sisters?"

"My father's name was Jacob, but we were not always happy family because ... zzz."

Read Genesis chapter 37, verses 3 to 4 to find out why Joseph's family was not happy.

Joseph

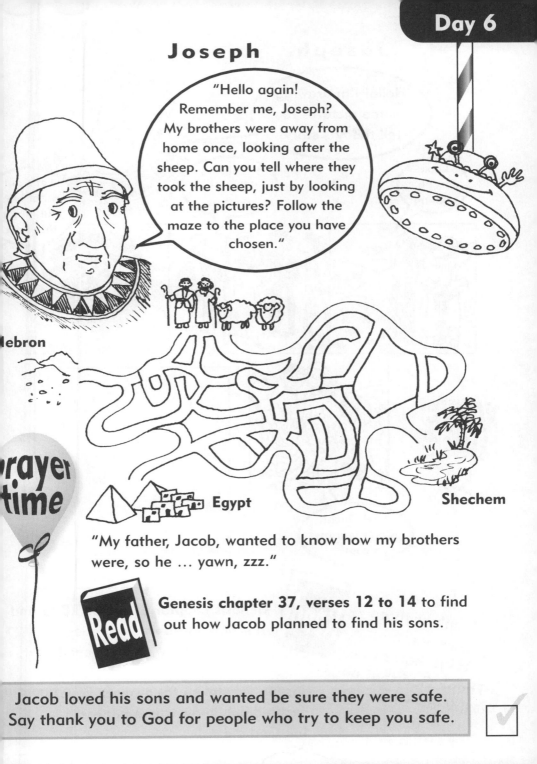

"Hello again! Remember me, Joseph? My brothers were away from home once, looking after the sheep. Can you tell where they took the sheep, just by looking at the pictures? Follow the maze to the place you have chosen."

Hebron

Prayer time

Egypt

Shechem

"My father, Jacob, wanted to know how my brothers were, so he ... yawn, zzz."

Read Genesis chapter 37, verses 12 to 14 to find out how Jacob planned to find his sons.

Jacob loved his sons and wanted be sure they were safe. Say thank you to God for people who try to keep you safe.

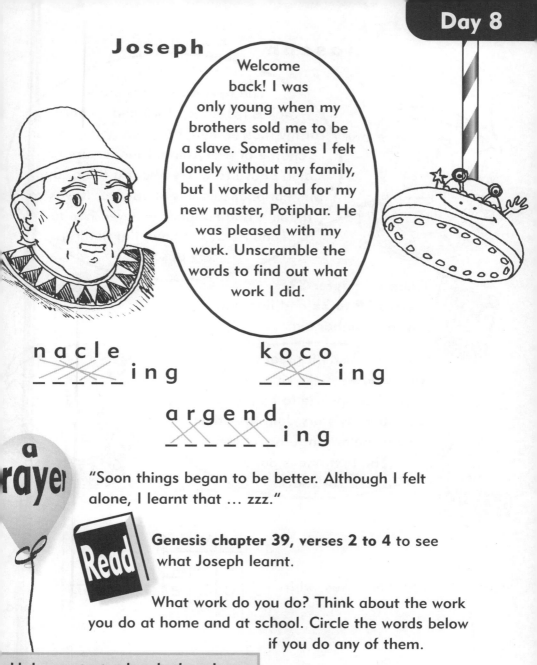

Joseph

Welcome back! I was only young when my brothers sold me to be a slave. Sometimes I felt lonely without my family, but I worked hard for my new master, Potiphar. He was pleased with my work. Unscramble the words to find out what work I did.

n a c l e
_ _ _ _ _ ing

k o c o
_ _ _ _ ing

a r g e n d
_ _ _ _ _ _ ing

a Prayer

"Soon things began to be better. Although I felt alone, I learnt that … zzz."

Read — Genesis chapter 39, verses 2 to 4 to see what Joseph learnt.

What work do you do? Think about the work you do at home and at school. Circle the words below if you do any of them.

Help me to try hard when I am working, Lord God, whether I like the work or not. Thank you for helping me.

sums
writing
tidying
feeding animals
cleaning

Joseph

Hello again.
The next part of my story
makes me angry. I worked so hard
for my master, Potiphar, that he put me in
charge of everything. I made sure he
didn't have to worry about a thing. But
Mrs Potiphar told lies about me. It was so
unfair – and Potiphar believed her lies!
Then he … Oh dear, I'm getting
very upset…

Read Genesis chapter 39,
verses **19 to 22** and find out
what Potiphar did.

Wasn't it great
that God was still with me? Try
this word puzzle to help you
remember my story. Join the other
words below on to my name.
The first one is done
for you.

prayer

The Lord ~~was~~ with

		w				
		a				
J	o	s	e	p	h	
		o				

Lord God, you are with me too, even when
things are unfair, even when I'm angry or upset.
Help me to remember your love and care.

Joseph

"Hello! Did you dream last night? While I was in prison, two men asked me what their dreams meant. Nobody knows that except God! He helped me to understand. I said to one of the men, 'If you get out of prison before me, tell the king that I'm here because someone told lies about me.' But he forgot until the king himself had some dreams. One dream was about cows!"

Draw a fat cow by the thin one to show the king's dream.

"The king found out I had told people what their dreams meant and he sent for me. Mmm ... all this talk about dreams makes me feel sleepy ... zzz."

prayer time

Read

Genesis chapter 41, verse 15 to 16 and see what the king said to Joseph.

What do you have to do that you find hard? Talk to God about it and ask him to help you.

Joseph could not explain the dreams on his own, but he knew God could do it.

☑

Joseph

"Do you remember how God helped me to understand the king's dream? What an exciting day that was! God told me that the fat cows meant that there would be seven good years when we would grow lots of food. The thin cows meant that in the next seven years not much would grow. The king needed someone to organise storing the extra food in the seven good years, ready to sell in the bad years. Guess who he chose to do that! He said to me:"I appoint you governor of all Egypt!

I'd started the day as a prisoner and ended it as governor of the whole country! God had a plan to make me important and help many people in those seven bad years.

Read Genesis chapter 41, verse 42. Circle the things the king gave Joseph.

a **prayer**

Dear Lord God, how clever and wonderful you are. You never let us down and all your plans for us are good. I praise you!

Joseph

In the seven good years, plenty of food was stored away. It was a busy time, but the next seven years were even busier. Every day, people came to ask if they could buy food. I usually let them have what they wanted. But some were spies, trying to steal our stores of food. One day, some men came who had travelled a long ... long ... way. I was amazed because they were ... zzz

Who were they?

LOOk up

Genesis chapter 42, verses 5 to 7.

How do you think Joseph felt about his brothers? Look back to Day 7 to see what they had done to him.

prayer time

Solve the muddled words and draw a circle around the one which shows how you think Joseph might have felt.

Think of times when you have been angry with your family. Ask God to help you forgive them. Remember to show them that you still love them, even when they have upset you.

Joseph

When my brothers came to Egypt, one of them was missing. It was Benjamin, who was only a boy the last time I saw him. I wanted him to come to Egypt, so I pretended to be cross with my brothers and played a trick on them. (They didn't guess who I was!) I sold them some food, but kept Simeon in prison until they returned with Benjamin. I found out later that my father, Jacob, was unhappy when he heard this. He didn't want Benjamin to go, but in the end they had no more food. So, while I'm having a little sleep … zzz.

Read **Genesis chapter 43, verses 1 to 5** and see what happened.

What do you think Jacob said to Joseph's brothers as they set off for Egypt? Write or say what you think.

When we leave someone, we often say, "Goodbye." This means "God bless you" or "God make you happy."

Who would you like to ask God to bless? Think of your family and friends and ask God to bless them all.

Joseph

My story is nearly over. Now we come to the really happy bit! When I saw Benjamin and my other brothers again, I was full of joy. But I didn't tell them who I was at first. I waited until we were quite alone together and then I said, 'I am Joseph. Is Jacob, our father, still alive?' They were so surprised! Then they began to look afraid. Perhaps they thought I was still angry because they had sold me as a slave all those years before. So I said ... zzz.

Read

Genesis chapter 45, verses 4 to 5 to find out what Joseph said next.

prayer time

Tick the sentences that are true and cross out the ones that are not true.

- Joseph put all his brothers in prison.
- Joseph said that his brothers should not blame themselves.
- God had forgotten all about Joseph and his family.
- God had planned to save people's lives when there was no food.

Lord God, you are great. I am so glad that you are looking after me, especially when

Joseph

At last, I was back with my family again. There was just one more person that I longed to see. In the pattern below, colour in every shape that has a dot in it to find out who it was.

Genesis chapter 45, verses 16 to 18 and find out what happened next.

prayer time

What a happy day it was when I saw my father again! I was sure then that God had been looking after us all the time. Even when things had seemed to go wrong for me, God had been working out his plan for us. Now my story is over. If you want to read more about it, turn to the next page. Goodbye! God bless you. (I kept awake right to the end today!)

What did you like best about the story of Joseph? Tell someone and then thank God for the Bible which has so many good stories in it.

Extra!

This page is for **extra-ordinary** readers. You could do some of these extra readings on your own or ask someone to read them to you. Before you begin, make a Joseph bookmark so that you don't have to keep looking for Genesis every time you want to read more about Joseph. You could copy this pattern:

Tick the box when you have read each part of the story.

☐ Joseph the dreamer **Genesis chapter 37, verses 1 to 36.**

☐ Working for Potiphar **Genesis chapter 39, verses 1 to 6.**

☐ In prison **Genesis chapter 39, verses 19 to 23, and chapter 40, verses 1 to 15.**

☐ Joseph and the king **Genesis chapter 41, verses 1 to 32.**

☐ Joseph, the governor of Egypt **Genesis chapter 41, verses 33 to 49, and verses 53 to 57.**

☐ Joseph's brothers come to buy food **Genesis chapter 42, verses 1 to 24.**

☐ Going home for Benjamin **Genesis chapter 42, verses 25 to 38.**

☐ Jacob, Benjamin and the return to Egypt **Genesis chapter 43, verses 1 to 34.**

☐ The missing cup **Genesis chapter 44, verses 1 to 34.**

☐ Joseph tells his brothers who he is **Genesis chapter 45, verses 1 to 24.**

☐ Jacob learns that Joseph is alive **Genesis chapter 45, verses 25 to 28.**

☐ All together in Egypt **Genesis chapter 46, verses 28 to 34, and chapter 47, verses 1 to 12.**

Perhaps you could make a picture book about Joseph's story. ☑

I can pray for other people

It was festival time in Jerusalem, but the Christians there were too worried to celebrate. Soldiers had come and arrested Peter. They had taken him into the prison and locked the big iron gates. Inside he was chained up and there were always four soldiers on duty to guard him. Poor Peter was in bad trouble. All seemed hopeless.

Read **Acts chapter 12, verses 4 and 5** to find out what Peter's friends did.

Cross out the things that Peter did NOT have.

prison	soldiers	party	chains
holiday	flowers	guards	teddy

prayer time

Now fit the letters in **dark type** in the words that are left into these spaces.

Peter's friends _ _ _ y e _ for him.

Do you know someone who is sick, sad or in trouble? Write in the person's name and use this prayer whenever you think of them. Please God help:

They prayed and prayed and went on praying. What do you think they would have asked God to do for Peter?

I can pray for other people

Do you remember that Peter was in prison? His friends went on praying and praying.

One night when Peter was asleep in prison, chained and guarded, something amazing happened.

Read about it in **Acts chapter 12, verses 6 to 10.**

What happened? Can you number the pictures in the right order?

Peter puts on his sandals.

An angel appears.

The iron gates open.

Peter and the angel walk down the street.

The chains fall off.

prayer time

Peter thought he was dreaming! What a wonderful God we have who listens to us and answers our prayers!

Thank God for listening to your prayers. Don't forget to keep praying!

I can pray for other people

Can you join these people to what they are expecting?

Peter didn't expect to be let out of prison. But when he found himself in the street, he realised that he was really free. He ran to the home of his friends and banged on the door. But what happened?

prayer time

Read Acts chapter 12, verses 13 to 17 to find out.

Peter's friends didn't believe that Peter was at the door. They weren't expecting God to answer their prayers in such a wonderful way.

Thank God for always answering your prayers, even if it's in a way you don't expect. Think of one answer to prayer you have had and say a special thank you.

God always hears us when we pray but he doesn't always answer in the way we expect!

I can pray for other people

Paul was a great traveller. Everywhere he went he told people the Good News about Jesus. In every place he left a group of friends who had learned to love Jesus. He often prayed for them and wrote letters to them.

Paul had happy memories of his stay in Philippi. The Christians there had been very kind to him and invited him to stay in their homes. He remembered wonderful times of worship together on the river bank.

Read what Paul wrote in his letter to them in **Philippians chapter 1, verses 3 and 4.**

Cross out all the 'and's.

Prayer time

What is the word hidden at the bottom?

Dear friends
Every and time and I and think and of and you and I and thank and my and God. Whenever I pray for you it makes me ha[

Who makes you happy when you think of them?
Father God, it makes me happy to think of
[   ]. Thank you specially for
them and all the people who make me happy.

I can pray for other people

When Paul visited Thessalonica, he told the people there about Jesus. Lots of them listened carefully to the Good News. Many of them became friends of Jesus.

In the letter Paul wrote later to these friends, he asked them to help him.

Read

2 Thessalonians, chapter 3 verse 1 to find out how Paul wanted them to help him.

Dear friends, Please p_ _ _ _ for us.

prayer time

They were very happy to know that their prayers would help Paul to tell more people about Jesus.

Which of these men is delivering Paul's letter?

Who tells you about Jesus? Say thank you to God for them and ask him to help them to tell more people about Jesus.

THESSALONICA

I can pray for other people

Dear

Write a letter
or draw a
picture for your
best friend.

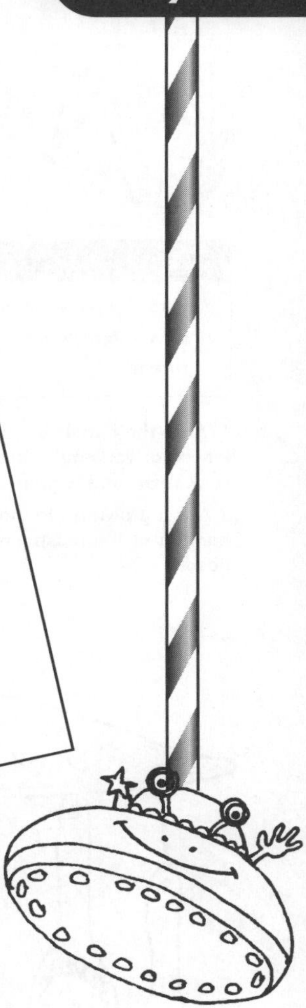

lots of love from

Prayer time

When Paul wrote a letter to his friends in the city of Corinth he ended it with a prayer for them. You can read Paul's prayer in **2 Corinthians, chapter 13, verse 13.**

Paul is asking God to give lots and lots of his love to each of them, and to always be with them. God's love is wonderful and very special. It helps us to love each other too. We often pray Paul's prayer in church for our friends.

Think about your friends. Use the words of **2 Corinthians chapter 13, verse 13** as a prayer for them

Make a prayer chime

to remind you to pray for
your friends.

You will need

- a strong paper-plate
- plastic teaspoons
- thread

- a lolly stick
- small sticky labels
- pens or crayons

1 Write the initials of your friends on the labels (or you could draw their faces) and stick them on the spoons.

2 Ask a grown-up to make holes in the handles of the teaspoons with a large heated needle.

3 Fix the spoons to the rim of the plate with thread. Hang the lolly stick in the middle.

4 Hang your chime near an open window to catch the breeze. Every time you hear the sound, you can remember to pray for your friends.

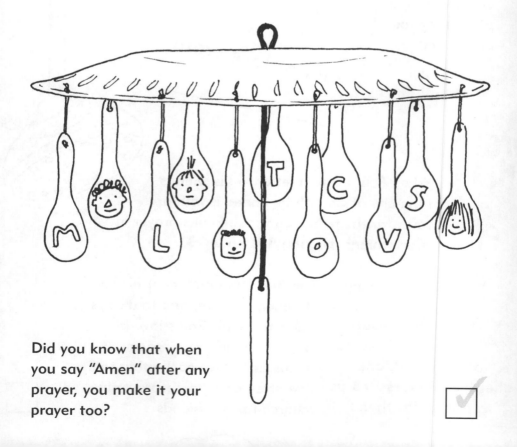

Did you know that when you say "Amen" after any prayer, you make it your prayer too?

Onesimus

Meet Paul's friend, Philemon. He loved Jesus, and was kind and generous to the other Christians in his town. He had a big house and lots of slaves to look after it.

But Philemon was cross! One slave called Onesimus had done wrong and run away.

> Onesimus – that name means "useful". But he has let me down. He's useless to me.

One day Onesimus turned up again and, surprise, surprise, he gave Philemon a letter from Paul! Read what Paul had written in his letter in **Philemon verses 4 and 5.**

> Oh dear, Paul is in prison. He is still praying for me. That's wonderful! But I'm still annoyed with useless Onesimus.

prayer time

Can you add three things to make this useless bicycle useful?

How would you feel to hear that a friend is praying for you? Think of a friend that you haven't seen for some time. Ask God to take care of them.

Onesimus

Onesimus the runaway slave had travelled a very long way to Rome. There he met Paul. Even though Paul was in prison, he was still talking about Jesus.

Onesimus heard the Good News. He became a friend of Jesus. He was really sorry that he had done wrong and asked God to forgive him. Now he was useful and helped to look after Paul.

God has forgiven me, but I must go back and say sorry to Philemon too. I'm scared! I deserve to be punished.

In his letter Paul asked Philemon to welcome Onesimus back as a useful friend. Read this in **Philemon verses 15 and 16.**

a prayer

I'm sorry I've dropped your car.

I forgive you.

I'll never speak to you again.

Jesus, please help me to show my love for you by the way I treat my friends, even when I feel cross with them.

Come and play tomorrow.

Let's try to mend it

God wanted Philemon to forgive and forget too. Draw yourself here. Then tick the answers God would like you to give.

The place to meet God

We can worship God anywhere: in our homes, outside in a wood, or even on a beach. But God loves people to come together and worship him as a group or family of believers. The Bible talks about the Church being a family with God as Father.

Where do you go to worship God? Write down the name of your church.

Did you know that the first place that was made for God was a tent? The people were travelling around and needed to be able to carry it with them. God gave Moses a plan on how to build it. Look it up in **Exodus chapter 25, verses 8 and 9.**

a **prayer** of

Plans are important when you build. This man did not look at his plans properly, and his house has come out all topsy-turvy! Help him to rebuild it.

Choose one of the favourite songs you sing at church and sing it to God as a prayer.

The place to meet God

The special tent for God had been made. It had taken a lot of hard work, but it was worth it. The Israelites knew that God was near them. They knew that he would always be with them.

 in **Exodus chapter 40, verses 34 to 38** to fill in the blanks below. Then finish the pictures.

l u c d o

The _ _ _ _ was over the tent in daytime,

e r f i

and the _ _ _ _ was burning at night.

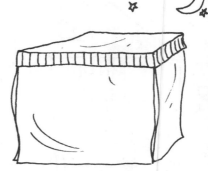

prayer time

We may not be able to see God, but many things in life can remind us that he is near. What reminds you of God? The rushing wind? A rainbow? Singing birds?

Draw some things that remind you that God is with you and thank him for always being near.

Extra!

Have you ever been camping? It's great fun to sleep outdoors in a tent. But you could also make a tent inside your own house!

Ask a grown-up to put together some chairs with a sheet or blanket over them. Now you can crawl into your own tent.

Put another sheet over the carpet, and ask if you can have a meal or snack inside your tent.

Other good things to do in a tent:

- Be cosy and warm
- Sing songs
- Let weary travellers (family or teddies) come in for rest
- Plan a visit to the next village (kitchen or bedroom)

Have fun in your tent!

Day 26

The place to meet God

Do you remember that God had given Moses a plan for building a tent? When the Israelite people were settled in Judah, they wanted to make a proper building to worship God in.

Solomon was king, and he was now going to build a special place for the worship of God. Do you know who Solomon's father was?

Read **1 Kings, chapter 5, verses 3 to 5** to find who he was and what God had promised him.

What was Solomon going to build? Fit the words into the sentences and the grid and read the word you have made downwards.

1 We must _ _ _ _ _ in God.

2 King _ _ _ _ _ _ _ started building.

3 The Lord made a _ _ _ _ _ _ _ to David.

4 Solomon said, "I worship the _ _ _ _".

a prayer

trust

Lord

Promise

Solomon

e

e

Thank you, Father God, that we can go to our church building and worship you there.

The place to meet God

Do you have a friend who likes to help you? King Solomon did. His name was Hiram, and he was king of a place called Tyre.

When Hiram found out that Solomon was building a temple for God, he wanted to help.

Read **1 Kings chapter 5, verses 9 and 10,** and write down what types of trees Hiram cut down to make logs.

C _ _ _ _

P _ _ _

a
rayer

Help Hiram's men to get the logs
safely to Solomon.

Thank you, God, for the good friends I have,
especially those who help me to know you better.

The place to meet God

Have you ever been near to a building site? The noise is so loud that many builders wear protection around their ears in case they lose their hearing. Sometimes mistakes happen because no-one can hear anyone else talk.

Do you think it was noisy at the site where Solomon's men were building the temple? Read **1 Kings chapter 6, verse 7** to find out.

Do you think Solomon wanted the temple site to be quiet because it was a

e i p l a c s

_ _ _ _ _ _ _ place for God?

Draw a circle around all the things that are quiet, and put a cross through all the noisy things.

prayer time

Thank God for the quiet and special times you can spend with him.

The place to meet God

In the temple King Solomon's men had built for God, everywhere was beautiful. The inside walls were decorated with carvings of animals, palm trees and flowers.

1 Kings chapter 6, verses 29 and 30 to find out what the floor was covered with. _ _ _ _

How would you decorate a room specially for God? What colours would you use?

Can you draw one part of your room here?

God has given us lots of lovely colours. Which is your favourite? Thank God for all the beautiful colours that we can see.

The place to meet God

The temple was finished. It had taken a long time and a lot of effort to make it just right.

Solomon prayed to God in front of all the people. It was a very special day.

Read part of Solomon's prayer in **1 Kings chapter 8, verses 27 to 30.**

How long would you take to celebrate a special event? In verse 65 the Bible says that the people of Israel celebrated the dedication of the temple for seven days!

Colour in the bricks with dots to see what Solomon did at the temple.

P	R	S.	L.	A	O.	Y
T.	E	A.	D	F.	T	O
X.	M.	G	I.	O	B.	D

Be like Solomon. Make a prayer to praise God. Thank him for your church, and the special things that happen there.

The place to meet God

The people who wrote the psalms loved going to worship God so much that they wrote songs about it. Singing has always been an important part in worshipping God. Do you like singing?

We read in **Psalm 84, verses 1 to 3** that even the birds lived and sang near the temple. What sorts of birds were they?

s _ a _ _ ows and s _ a _ _ ows

Can you find two birds the same? Draw circles round them.

prayer time

When we think of all the things that God has done for us, it is easy to want to praise him. Praise God today for all the good things in your life, and write or draw some of them here.

Extra!

There are many different styles of church building. How many can you think of? Many churches use stained-glass windows. Long ago, this was a way of showing stories from the Bible to people who could not read.

You can make your own stained-glass window by collecting see-through sweet wrappers or coloured tissue-paper.

First, make your background picture out of black card. You could use the design below, or make up your own one. Cut out the holes very carefully.

Cut your pieces of colour into small shapes, and stick them onto your card over the holes.

When it's finished, you could hang it in front of a window and see the sun lighting up your picture.

All over the world!

All over the world people worship God in different places. Where do you go to worship God? Is it like any of these places here?

Some places are very old, like this church in England.

Some places are quite new, like these buildings in Zimbabwe and England.
(Which do you think is which?)

Some places are in the open air! These people are under a tree in Malaysia.

Some places look very exciting, like this Bible bus in Germany

Draw the place where you worship God here.

Say thank you to God for all the people who worship there with you.

Jesus does amazing things

Jesus did lots of amazing things while he was on earth. We're going to learn about some of them on the next few days.

One amazing thing happened at the Pool of Bethzatha in Jerusalem. Sometimes the water would bubble up. Many people believed that when this happened, the first person to get into the water would be healed of whatever was wrong with them.

John chapter 5, verses 3 and 4 to find out what sort of people went to the pool.

Can you draw some of them around the pool?

Dear Jesus, please be close to people who are sick or disabled, especially

Jesus does amazing things

One day Jesus went to the Pool of Bethzatha. He saw a man who could not walk.

Read **John chapter 5, verse 5** to find out how long he had been unable to walk.

Join up the dots to make the number of years.

What a long time! Jesus felt sorry for the man.

Don't you want to get well?

No, I prefer to lie down.

Yes, but I'm a bad man. I won't be healed.

a prayer

Yes, but I don't have anyone to help me into the water.

Yes, but I'm waiting until I'm older.

Thank you, Jesus, that you care about each one of us.

Read **verse 7**, then cross out the wrong answers.

Jesus does amazing things

Jesus knew that bubbling water couldn't make a person better. But he knew who could! He told the man at the pool to do something very strange. (Remember he could not walk.)

John chapter 5, verse 8 to find out what it was. Then check your answer by crossing out every **j** and **g** in the sentence below.

> gpickjjgupg
> jyourjgjmatjgand
> ggwalkjg

a prayer

Read **verse 9** and draw what happened next.

The man didn't argue with Jesus. He did exactly what Jesus told him to, even though it must have seemed very strange.

> Dear Jesus, help me to do what you tell me to in the Bible.

Jesus does amazing things

Another amazing thing that Jesus did happened near water too, this time by the side of Lake Galilee.

Jesus had spent a busy day teaching the people about God and healing the sick. He was very tired and needed a rest. So he and his special friends crossed over the lake.

LOOk up John chapter 6, verses 3 and 4 to see where they went.

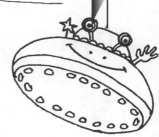

a prayer

Did Jesus get a rest? **Read verse 5** to find out who had followed him.

Draw them coming towards Jesus.

Soon Jesus was surrounded by a huge crowd. It was getting late and they were all hungry!

Jesus was concerned about them. What could they do? Where could they get enough food?

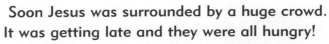

Thank you, Jesus, that you always care about others. Help me to put others first too.

Jesus does amazing things

Do you ever go out into the countryside for a day? What sort of things do you like to take to eat? Draw them in the lunch box.

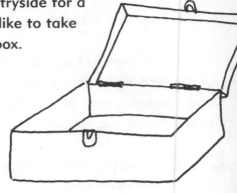

The people in our story were so interested in hearing what Jesus had to say that they forgot all about bringing something to eat. There was just one little boy who had brought a picnic.

Read **John chapter 6, verse 9** to find what he had to eat.

Draw it here.

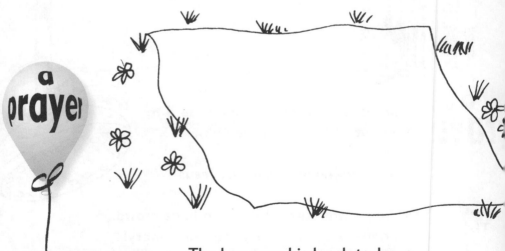

Dear Jesus, help me to be willing to share my things with others.

The boy gave his lunch to Jesus. But it wasn't much good for all those people. Or was it? Remember that Jesus could do amazing things.

Jesus does amazing things

What was Jesus going to do with the little boy's lunch?

1st He told his friends to make all the people sit down.

LOOk up John chapter 6, verse 10 to find out

how many men there were in the crowd.

Answer: [   ] thousand!! (And that's not counting the women and children!)

2nd He said thank you to God for the fish and bread.
3rd He gave the food to the people.

But surely there wasn't enough for all those people?
Read **verse 11** to find out what happened.

Everyone had

Colour in
the correct
answer.

*prayer
time*

Wasn't that amazing?

The little boy offered his food to Jesus. Jesus was able to feed the whole crowd with it. What could you do for Jesus? It doesn't have to be anything big or difficult.

Thank you, Jesus, that you can use little children. Please show me what I can do for you.

Jesus does amazing things

Jesus had fed all the people with just five loaves and two fish. Eventually everyone was full up. They couldn't eat another crumb. But there was still lots of food left over. Jesus didn't want good food to be wasted, so he told his friends to pick up the left-over pieces.

John chapter 6, verse 13 to find out how many baskets they filled.

Can you find them all hidden in the picture below? Colour them in.

a prayer

Wasn't Jesus amazing? I expect the little boy was surprised that his picnic was enough for over 5,000 people, don't you?

Dear Jesus, thank you that I have plenty to eat. Help me not to waste food or to be greedy, and to remember people who are often hungry.

Extra!

Make your own rolls

Why don't you make some little loaves like the boy offered to Jesus? (This recipe won't feed 5,000 though!) You will need to ask a grown-up to help you.

You will need

- 1½ lbs (750g) strong white flour
- 1 ounce (25g) lard
- 1 sachet easy-blend yeast
- 2 teaspoons (10 ml) salt
- ¾ pint (450 ml) warm water

1 Heat the oven to 230° C.

2 Put the flour and salt into a large bowl.

3 Rub* in the lard, then mix in the yeast.

4 Add the water and mix. Knead* for 5 – 10 minutes on a floured surface. Put back in the bowl, cover and leave in a warm place until the dough has doubled in size.

5 Re-knead for a few minutes. Then divide the dough into 12 and shape into rolls. Leave until the rolls have doubled in size.

6 Cook for approximately 15 minutes.

* Ask a grown-up to show you what these words mean.

You could try different types of rolls, eg plaits, cottage loaves or even your initials.

When you eat your rolls (make sure they aren't too hot or you will get indigestion!), remember the little boy who gave his food to Jesus.

Jesus does amazing things

Jesus always noticed people who needed his help. One day as he was walking along he saw a man who had a very difficult life and definitely needed help. Do the puzzle below to find out what the problem was, then look up **John chapter 9, verse 1** to check your answer.

The man was

In fact he had been born blind, so had never seen the beautiful world God had made, nor his family or friends.

In those days life was very difficult for blind people. The man could not work and so had to beg for money to buy food. What would Jesus do? Would he give the man some money?

a prayer

Thank you, Jesus, that you notice each one of us and know just what we need.

Jesus does amazing things

Do you remember that Jesus met a blind man? Something amazing happened, something which changed his life for ever.

wash

Later on the man's friends asked him what Jesus had done.

eyes

Read **John chapter 9, verse 11** to find out what he replied.

Fill in the missing words. You will find them hidden around the page.

Jesus made some ⬳ and put it on my ⬭

. Then he told me to ⬙ it off in

the ▭ of Siloam. When I did I

could ◇ The man was so happy

that he became a follower

of Jesus.

see

rayer ime

Jesus, you are amazing. I praise you especially for

▭

Draw his face with his eyes wide open.
Draw a big smile on his face.

Pictures of Jesus

Bread for breakfast,
Bread for me.
It's delicious
With my tea.

Toast or sandwich,
Hot or cold,
Fresh and crumbly,
One hour old.

Bread's **important**,
As we know,
Tastes so **good** and
Helps me grow.

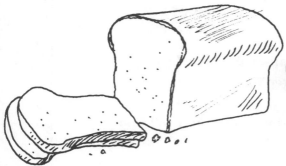

John chapter 6, verse 35 to see what Jesus said about bread.

Jesus did not mean that he is bread! He is like bread in some ways, but not in others. Look at the poem again. Some of the words in the last verse fit in below. Finish writing them.

a prayer

Jesus is _ m _ _ _ t _ _ t to me.

Jesus is _ o o _ to me.

Jesus h _ _ p _ m _ _ _ _ w.

Jesus helps us to grow into people who please God. What could you do today or tomorrow to please God?

Dear Jesus, help me to please God, today and always – to be kind, loving and generous just like you are.

Pictures of Jesus

I trod on my toys, I tripped over the cat,
Walking around in my bedroom last night;
Bumped into a chair, banged my head on a shelf.
I wish I'd remembered to turn on the light!

Why is it difficult
walking around in the
dark? Why do we
need light?

Read **John chapter 8, verse 12** to see what Jesus said about light.

Jesus is like a light in lots of ways.
Follow the lines to see how each light helps us.

Helps us find
the best way
in the dark.

Stops us
running into
danger.

Shows us
how beautiful
the world is.

Jesus helps us in just the same ways.
He is the light of the world.

Jesus, light of the world, stop us running into danger;
help us find the best way when life is difficult and
dark; thank you for making our beautiful world.

Did you know?

The sun is the brightest light we have. Even on cloudy days, the sun's light helps us to see. At night, when the earth isn't facing the sun, the moon shines because it is reflecting the sun's light. So, by day and by night, the sun gives us light.

Make your own sun to put up in your room.

You will need

- a large piece of card or strong paper
- a large round plate
- a pencil or a pen
- scissors
- yellow, orange and gold paper cut into small pieces
- a glue-stick or paste

1 On the card or paper, draw around the plate. Cut out the circle.

2 Cover part of the circle in glue or paste.

3 Quickly, before the glue dries, stick on the pieces of paper.

4 Repeat this, until the circle is covered.

5 If you like, make the sun's rays from strips of coloured card pasted to the back of the sun.

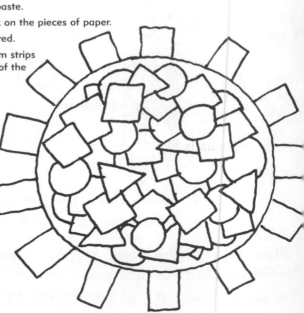

When your sun is dry, pin it up in your room.

When you look at your sun, remember that Jesus is the light of the world. He is with us day and night.

Pictures of Jesus

A good shepherd

A bad shepherd

What differences can you see in the two pictures? If you were a sheep, which shepherd would you like to look after you?

Read John chapter 10, verse 4 to see what Jesus said about shepherds.

Jesus is like a shepherd in lots of ways, though he looks after us, not just sheep! He knows us all and understands how we feel whether we are happy or sad.

a **rayer**

Dear Jesus, thank you for being like a good shepherd to me. I'm glad that you know me. Help me to know you and love you every day.

Pictures of Jesus

Do this puzzle to find out the name of each sheep.

Bob is eating grass.
Babs is next to Bob.
Baa is sitting down.
Boo is on the end of the line.

Now you know the sheep's names! And so does their shepherd.
He knows when the sheep are hurt or ill. He is glad to see the
sheep and lambs playing happily in the field.

John chapter 10, verses 2 and 3 to
see what Jesus said about sheep and
their names. Then read **verse 14.**

Just as a good shepherd knows the names of the
sheep, so Jesus knows our names. He knows all about us.

Write your name here.

Tell Jesus that you are glad that
he knows your name. Say thank
you that he knows all about you
– your home, your family and
your friends.

Pictures of Jesus

Once there was a shepherd who had some sheep. He loved them all and looked after them carefully. If the sheep were attacked by a wolf, the shepherd chased it away, even though he knew that it might attack him.

One day, the shepherd had other work to do and couldn't look after the sheep himself, so he got someone to work for him. This hired man didn't care much for the sheep. He just wanted the money the shepherd would pay him.

What do you think would happen if the hired man saw the wolf coming?

Read **John chapter 10, verses 11 and 12** to find out.

The sheep were afraid of the wolf, but the good shepherd was there to protect them. And Jesus, who is our good shepherd, says:

a prayer

pqnoqponqepqpcapnqp
snpqaqtcqhpqpthpeqmpq
outqqopfqpmqypqphaqndp

Cross out all the p's and q's to find out what Jesus says in **John chapter 10, verse 28.**

Loving Jesus, it's good to know that you are my good shepherd. When I am afraid, I'm happy to know that you are with me.

Abraham

Abram (later he is called Abraham) lived in a place called Haran. He had a wife and lots of relatives but no children of his own. God spoke to Abraham and gave him some instructions.

Read **Genesis chapter 12, verses 1 and 2** to find out what God wanted Abraham to do.

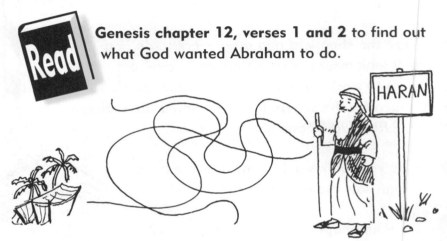

God told Abraham to go to a new country. God said that he would give Abraham many children and make him famous.

a prayer Can you find which way Abraham went to get to his new home?

How would Abraham know the way to go? Look in **Genesis chapter 12, verse 1.**

God said

l i w l   w o s h   u y o

I _ _ _   _ _ _ _   _ _ _

Father God, you love me just like you loved Abraham. Please help me to do the things you want me to do.

Abraham

Abraham was old. He did not have any children. One night he was walking outside his tent. He looked up at all the stars in the night sky and tried to count them. There were too many for him to count!

While Abraham was looking at the stars, God spoke to him. God made a promise to Abraham. What was the promise? You can find it in **Genesis chapter 15, verse 5.**

Abraham listened to God's promise. How could he have many descendants when he hadn't got even one child ("descendants" means people in his family)?

Did Abraham believe God's promise? Read **Genesis chapter 15, verse 6** to find out. Write the answer in the stars:

Lord

believed

the

Something to do
On a dark night go outside and look at the stars. How many are there? Can you count them? God promised there would be more people in Abraham's family than stars in the sky!

a prayer

Thank you, Father God, that Abraham trusted you and you were pleased with him. I want to please you too. Please help me to trust you.

Abraham

One hot day, as Abraham was sitting in the shade outside his tent, he saw three men standing there. He went to meet them.

Read the story in **Genesis chapter 18, verses 1 to 5.**

Put a tick in the box by the things which are true and a cross in the box by the things that are not true.

☐ Abraham was sitting in a house.

☐ Abraham was sitting outside his tent.

☐ He saw three men.

☐ He saw five men.

☐ Abraham hid from the men.

☐ Abraham ran out to meet them.

☐ The men washed their feet.

☐ The men washed their hands.

☐ Sarah, Abraham's wife, gave the visitors something to eat and drink and they had a rest.

a prayer

Abraham and Sarah were kind to their visitors. Draw circles round the children who are being kind.

Father God, help me to be kind and thoughtful to the people who live in my home and the people who come to visit it.

Abraham

Can you remember that Abraham and his wife had some special visitors? Sarah made some bread for the men to eat. She heard them tell Abraham that she was going to have a baby.

Abraham and Sarah were very old. Sarah laughed and said that she was too old to have a baby.

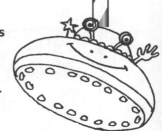

Read the story in **Genesis chapter 18, verses 13 and 14.**

What did God say? Check your answer by putting a mirror along the line.

Sɒɿɒ2 will ɒvɒʜ ɒ ƨon

Something to think about
God made a promise to Abraham. God also makes promises to us.

a prayer

Cross out every other letter then write the letters left over in the boxes.

Igakmnwhiftehaymocufaklfwsapyzs

What does God promise?

☐ ☐☐ ☐☐☐☐ ☐☐☐ ☐☐☐☐☐☐

Tell God that you are happy that he is always with you.

Abraham

God kept the promise he made to Abraham and Sarah. Sarah had a baby boy.

 the story in **Genesis chapter 21, verses 1 to 3** and find out what the baby was called. Make this look like the card that they could send to their friends.

A_____
and S_____
have a baby son.
The baby is called
I_____

Draw a picture of the baby here:

How do you think Abraham and Sarah felt?
Draw a circle round the words.

excited

miserable

scared

thankful

happy

Write or draw some things you can thank God for. Say your own thank you prayer to God.

They said thank you to God for baby Isaac.

The joke and puzzle page!

You have read about lots of people in this book. Can you find these names in the wordsearch? (They go forwards and backwards, down and up.) Can you remember the stories about these people?

ABRAHAM
NICODEMUS
SOLOMON
JOSEPH
PETER
SARAH
ONESIMUS
PHILEMON
JESUS
JACOB
POTIPHAR
PAUL

```
G N I C O D E M U S
E N E S N L U A P N
H R E T E P I H S O
P E X O S A R A H M
E D U S I P S R J E
S O L O M O N B A L
O A L M U S A A C I
J E S U S C T S O H
R A H P I T O P B P
```

When you have found all the names, write the letters that are left over in order here, to see some of the books of the Bible you have read from.

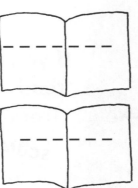

Animal holiday fun!

How do you know an elephant is going on holiday?
He will have his pyjamas packed in his trunk!

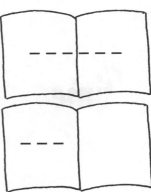

Where do leopards like to go on an adventure holiday? A spot they haven't seen before!

Which country would a big fish choose to visit? Wales!

Look out for more **Join in – Jump on!** books.

If you feel you're ready to move on from **Join in – Jump on!**, try **Snapshots**. It's great!

All available from Scripture Union

For more information ring 01908 856006 or contact your national office